HERMAN'S
magical
UNIVERSE

Becky McCarley

Illustrated by Phil Travers

for the evolving human spirit

HAMPTON ROADS
PUBLISHING COMPANY, INC.

This book is dedicated to my dad,

Dan McCarley, Sr.
1927–1997

Thank you, Daddy, for the Magic.

Text copyright © 1999 by Becky McCarley
Illustrations copyright © 1999 by Phil Travers

Cover design by Marjoram Productions
Cover art by Phil Travers
Line drawings by Rebecca Whitney

Bentov Model on page 25 used with permission of
Destiny Books, Rochester, Vermont.

For information write:

Hampton Roads Publishing Company, Inc.
134 Burgess Lane
Charlottesville, VA 22902

Or call: 804-296-2772
FAX: 804-296-5096
e-mail: hrpc@hrpub.com
Web site: http://www.hrpub.com

If you are unable to order this book from your local
bookseller, you may order directly from the publisher.
Quantity discounts for organizations are available.
Call 1-800-766-8009, toll-free.

Library of Congress Catalog Card Number: 98-73920

ISBN 1-57174-114-3

10 9 8 7 6 5 4 3 2 1

Printed on acid-free paper in the United States

ACKNOWLEDGMENTS

It would take another book to properly thank all those who have made this book possible. Indeed, I would have to list every single person and event of my life, for all have contributed something to who I am and thus, what I have written here.

So, all I can do is give back the best of what I have, to say thank you. I hope the gift of this writing begins to do that.

I must, however, choose a notable few who have been my greatest inspiration. I thank you Great Spirit most of all, that sweet Spirit who has upheld me and put this dream of His in my heart. I thank Him for finding me worthy to do this work, and for my dear Brother who lights my way.

I thank you Anita Norris for your clear guidance through the years and for giving me hope, when I had none of my own.

I thank you Lynn Buess, who saw it first.

I thank you Dusty Young, for the sound, the feel, of your "Do It," with the absolute knowing that I could.

I thank you Cynthia Rose Young Schlosser for first showing me what living in a state of grace looked like.

I thank you Grace King, for showing up, in person, right on time, when I had prayed for Grace. You are Grace to me.

I thank you Karen Ayers for being my first spiritual teacher and answering my questions by living the answers even more than by what you said.

I thank you Isa and Yolanda (Doc and Ruth) for being way-showers extraordinaire both past and present.

I thank you Ira Chase for always being there for me and for being the best friend anyone could ever hope for.

I thank you Harry H. Hann for first showing me, up close, what creative genius is made of. Your gift remains and grows.

I thank you Susan Martin for your Light in my darkness.

I thank you Sun Bear for your teaching and your love.

I thank you Crow.

I thank you Brenda Seabolt for asking that your place be the Lord's table and truly making it one. I thank you Sonny and Brenda and all your daughters, real and adopted—Dana, Jamie, Lisa, Kim, Linda, and Lorry—for adopting me and for feeding my body and my soul.

I thank Hermes and Dr. Fleet and the entire Concept-Therapy movement for putting it all in one place.

I thank you Myrna and Dave Brown for teaching me my first CT class and for loving me and answering my questions since then.

I thank you Lizzie Crabtree for reading the children's book manuscripts and passing mine on—even though they didn't publish children's books at that time.

I thank you Bob Friedman for saying "yes."

I thank you Jane Hagaman for your sweet, gentle, always positive and patient attitude which can even turn no's into yes's.

I thank you Pat Adler, Rebecca Williamson, Ken Eagle Feather, and Cynthia Mitchell for your dear kindness each time we have spoken and for all your contributions to this publishing process. Hampton Roads has attracted remarkable people and I look forward to meeting you all someday soon.

I also thank each and every person at Hampton Roads—those I've spoken to and those I've never spoken to or met (yet!) for every single thing you've done to bring this book into physical manifestation. God Bless You! You, your work, your daily contribution is remembered by me. I thank you.

My thanks to every book buyer, every distributor, every bookstore, every school, every library, every person and place associated in any way with getting this book into the hands of the children. You are blessed.

I thank you Phil Travers (whom I hunted down in England) for your perfect portrayal of "The Light." It was exactly what I was looking for and so much more. Your extraordinary gift blesses us all. I can't wait to meet you.

I thank you Dolores Rider, sweet soul sister, for all you've taught me and given me. Your friendship is such an honor to have. Joan lives—in us.

Emily, Linda, and Felicia, thank you for the family we made. I'll always remember you.

I thank all of you who have loved me well and given me your dear gifts of friendship, guidance, solace, and sustenance, laughter, questions, and answers.

I thank the two or three of you (you know who you are) who have made my path most difficult, for in overcoming your negativity, I have more fully claimed my self. My gratitude is immeasurable.

Thank you to each one of you on the Path who have held your lamps up high for me. This book is for you, the children, and all those who walk the Path. I look forward to seeing you all "up at the House." I love you all and I thank you all and I say thank you Great Spirit for loving me. I hope you are all well pleased.

Finally, I thank every single child of our sweet Earth who sent out the call and for choosing me to write down this answer. You will be the ones who will create "The Kingdom of God on Earth." I love you to the ends of infinity and more. Learn the Laws well, little brothers and sisters. Stand tall in the Light and stay in the Light. Be good and do right. You are the builders of the new Earth, long foretold by all religions.

This is my gift to you.
The best tool I have to give,
so that you may create

"Peace
on Earth as it is
in Heaven."

I want to tell you a story.

It's a true story.

It's your story.

Herman was a thoughtful child. His Momma said so. He wasn't absolutely sure what she meant by this, but it sounded somehow like it was not an altogether good thing. "Herman, you're too thoughtful. Go out and play!" or "Herman, quit moping around and go play!" He wasn't moping, he was trying to figure something out. Actually, it would be closer to the truth to say that Herman was getting mad. M-A-D, mad. Before, he was just curious, then a little aggravated—now he was getting downright mad. This is why.

When he got big enough to speak clearly—to make people understand what he was saying—he started asking a question. And NOBODY—not one single, solitary person he had asked—knew the answer. He quite simply wanted SOMEONE to tell him how the world worked. He knew there had to be some sort of rules for this, otherwise everything would be a big mess, like his room would get sometimes. But he knew how to put things back, nice and neat, and, once he had restored some order to his mess, he always felt better. So . . . he looked around him and saw that, for the most part, things seemed to be in order in the world, but sometimes they were really out of order. So he figured that, if they got fixed—which they often did—someone must have known HOW to fix them, so why wouldn't SOMEBODY tell him HOW THE WORLD WORKED!

At first he thought that maybe he was too little, that maybe you had to be a certain age and then somebody would tell you, but he had just had his seventh birthday party and no one gave him The Book. A book . . . he figured it all must be written down somewhere in a book and somebody would give him this book for his seventh birthday. Surely now he was old enough!

But no one did. He smiled graciously at the opening of each gift—they were nice gifts for a boy of seven—but really what he wanted, more than anything else . . . was The Book. Once, when he took one present in his hands to open it, he thought, yes, this is it. It's the right size for a book. It's heavy enough (The Book would be heavy with wisdom), and it is a present from my best friend. But no, it was only a couple of video games. He tried very hard not to look disappointed. But, to tell the truth, when his party was over and all his friends had gone and all the birthday cake was cleaned up off the floor, Herman quietly went to his room, shut his door, crawled up on his bed, hugged his cat Mudpie to him very hard, and cried.

Mudpie was puzzled. She had never seen Herman cry before. She didn't quite understand. What did tears mean? She licked a tear near Herman's chin and Herman smiled at her and snuggled her more. So she decided everything must be okay. She laid down then and got comfy. But Herman was not comfy.

He couldn't ever seem to be really comfortable again until he got The Book. He went to his teacher. He went to his sister. He went to his mother and father. He went to his best friend. He went to his grandfather. None of them knew what he was talking about.

Finally, he went to the school librarian, Diana. She did not want the children to call her "Mrs." anything. She insisted that everyone, even first-graders, call her Diana. She was very beautiful and a story was told about her that at home she had a pet owl, who would sometimes sit on her shoulder. Herman wondered if this was true.

He had all but lost hope entirely of ever knowing the Laws of Living when he approached Diana. She had been very busy, but, when she saw the sincerity in Herman's eyes, she immediately set aside everything she was doing and gave him her full attention.

"Yes Herman, how may I help you?"

"Diana," Herman said, "I have asked everyone I can think of, and no one knows the answer. Can you tell me where I might find the Laws of Living?"

At first Diana looked as though she would cry. Then her expression changed completely. She looked very, very deeply into Herman's eyes and said, "Herman, I have worked here in this library for twenty-nine years. I was here when your father and mother were children. There have been hundreds and hundreds of children who have come and gone from these halls of learning, and you, my dear, are the first one to ask this question. I have been waiting for you for a very long time." And then she looked at him with such joy in her eyes that Herman felt as though he had just done the best thing in all the world. She seemed so happy and proud of him that he couldn't help but feel happy and proud too.

But, quite honestly, he was just a bit confused. How could it be that no one before him had asked how to live properly? When he asked Diana this, she said, "Most people are too busy, Herman. They are rushing here and there—off to soccer practice, back from school, off to work, back from town—and they never give themselves 'alone time.' Alone time is good. Alone time is when you can stop and think about what's really important. Obviously, Herman, you have given yourself some alone time, so now let's see if we can answer your question."

And for the first time in a long, long while Herman felt deeply, truly, and completely happy. He was about to learn the Laws of Living and he knew that this would be the most important thing he would ever, ever know.

Diana walked to the back of the huge library and took down a big book from a very high shelf. She blew the dust off gently with her breath; then Diana told him a story, and this is what she said:

A long, long time ago, a very smart being named Hermes taught the Laws of Living to people. There are only seven. He told them that, if they would look carefully at the world around them, they would see these laws in operation. They could pay attention to the world and the way it worked and work with it, or they could ignore The Laws and go on about their business, taking their chances, or they could even live their lives working against The Laws if they wanted to. This is called "free will." It's a right we all have and can use in any way we choose. So, again, we can live any one of these three ways:

1. work with the universe

2. stay silly . . . or . . .

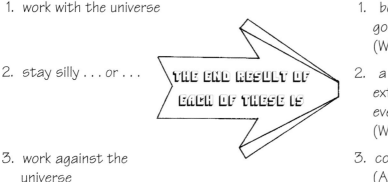
THE END RESULT OF EACH OF THESE IS

3. work against the universe

1. being in harmony, feeling good, being happy (WITH The Laws)

2. a life tossed from one extreme to the other and everything in between (WITHOUT The Laws)

3. confusion (AGAINST The Laws)

Now, going back to ol' Hermes, the smart ones took his advice and paid attention and found that, yes indeed, the same, simple, seven laws did apply to them as people and pets and plants and protons too. They found that, when they used the seven laws in their day-to-day lives, magical things happened. This magic is not something that can be described. It can only be experienced by the one practicing The Laws. If you do this, if you use The Laws, you will experience the magic too.

"Welcome to the Path of the Master."

This is what Diana said. And then, right there, in the Eustis Park Elementary School library, Diana placed "The Book" in Herman's hands. This is what The Book said:

THE SEVEN LAWS OF THE UNIVERSE

This universe is a seven system. The Great Celestial Parents created everything in our world—people, porcupines, and petunias—according to the same seven laws. This may seem surprising, considering all the differences in the world, but there really are only seven.

It helps to know The Laws, because when things aren't going right for us, we can figure out which law we're out of harmony with and then correct our course. When we get back in harmony with the seven laws the Great Celestial Parents gave us, then our lives are easier and happier.

It doesn't matter if you are a Buddhist or a Baptist, the seven laws work for us all. And just like gravity, it doesn't matter if we work with The Laws or against them; The Laws still operate.

The first thing to remember before you begin to use The Laws is that each of The Laws is an expression of One energy. In other words, the whole universe is made of energy. Everything is made of the same particles, just arranged in different ways. Puppy's ears are made of the same stuff that spaghetti is made of—energy. And your big toe is made of the same thing stars are made of—this same energy.

So the seven laws tell us how this energy works in our universe.

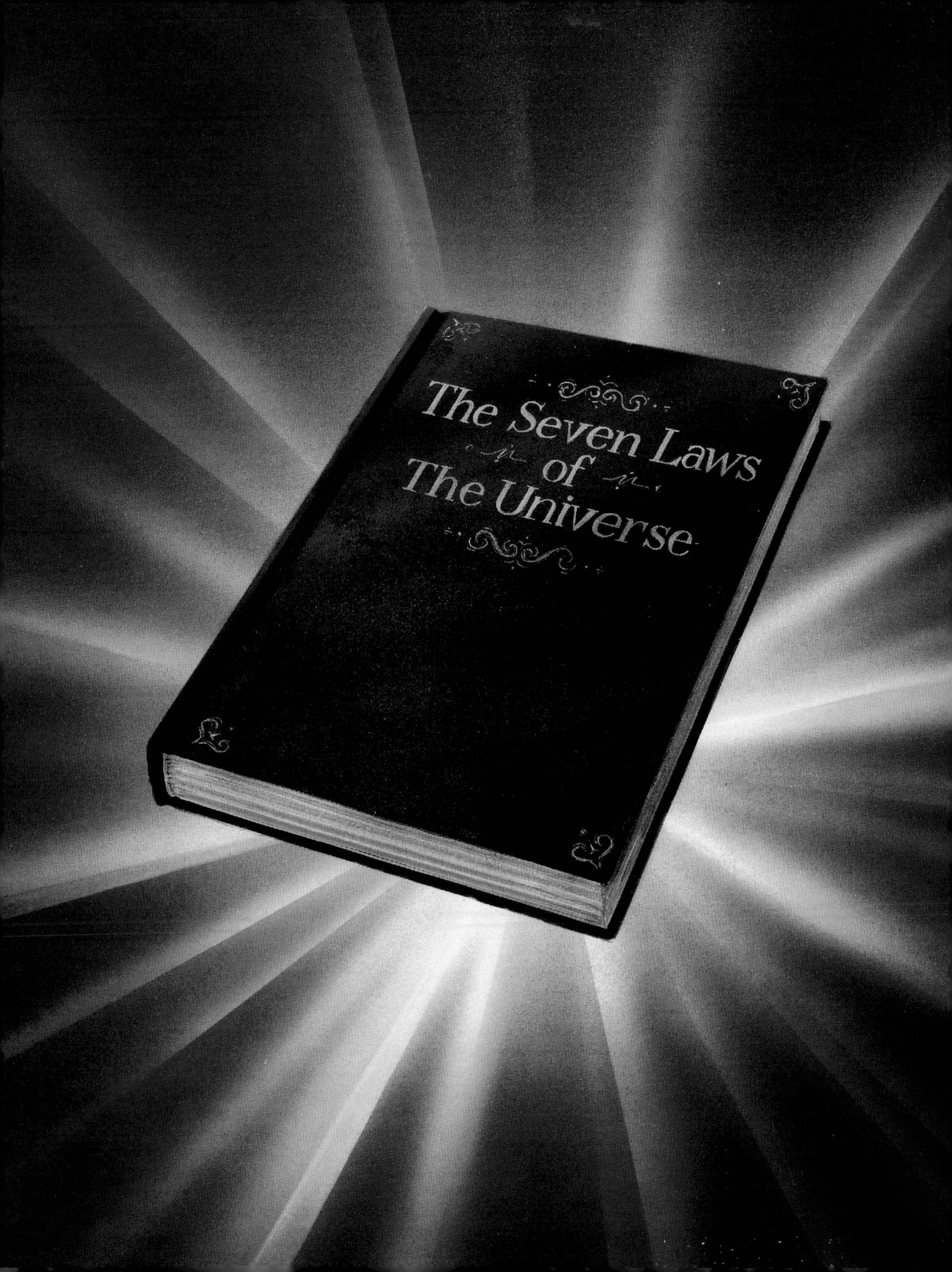
The Seven Laws of The Universe

The first law teaches us that ENERGY IS ALWAYS CHANGING. The only thing in the universe that never changes is that energy is always changing. Energy never sits still. It's always changing from one form to another form. A great scientist (you may have heard of him—Einstein) put it like this. He said, "Energy can neither be created nor destroyed, it simply changes form."

An acorn is the seed that grows up to become a great oak tree. The energy changes from being an acorn to being a tree—the leaves are green, then turn brown and fall off to eventually become the soil beneath the tree. See how the energy has changed form? The leaves haven't died. Nothing can die. It changes form.

This is what people do, too. No one ever really dies. They just change from one form to another form. What do you think the form looks like that we have after this one? I think it's bright and sparkly—like a light. What do you think?

What other things can you think of that change form?

ENERGY IS ALWAYS CHANGING.

The second law says that ALL THINGS ARE RELATIVE. This law can cheer you up fast. For example, if you stubbed your toe, you could whine and complain, or you could apply the law of relativity and realize that, if you had broken your leg, that would be much more terrible, so a stubbed toe wouldn't be so bad anymore—if you looked at it that way. And a broken leg wouldn't be so bad compared to something else.

So any situation is "relative" to any other situation in this way. You can always find a situation that's better or worse than the one you're in right now. You can look at the one that's better—to see where you might be, and you can look at the one that's worse—to see where you might be. "All things are relative" means that nothing is absolute. Everything is relative—all the time.

If you took a bite of an apple, and then you bit into an onion (yech!)—compared to the apple, the onion would taste quite bitter. Then, let's say you took a bite of the onion again, (yech! yech!) and THEN you bit into a big, juicy lemon! Compared to the lemon, the onion now tastes SWEET! So are you crazy or is this silly onion bitter or sweet?! IT'S RELATIVE.

But, if you're from Vidalia, Georgia, or thereabouts, then you gotta think of another example for this one. Everybody from Georgia knows what I mean.

Yes, Herman could hardly believe it too, but it actually said this—it mentioned Georgia—in the Laws of Living!

Now you understand the second law. Tricky, isn't it? But do you see how you can use it to cheer yourself up?

ALL THINGS ARE RELATIVE.

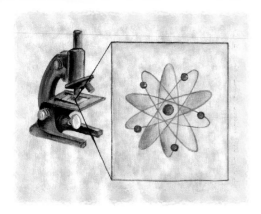

The third law is the LAW OF VIBRATION. This law tells us that energy vibrates or wiggles all the time. (Just like you, when you were two.) The faster it wiggles or vibrates, the more powerful it is. (Ask whoever tried to put on your socks when you were two.) Lasers, x-rays, and gamma rays, which vibrate very fast, can go right through rocks. But guess what the most powerful vibration is? Your thoughts! And one thought that is positive or happy is ten thousand times more powerful than any negative or unhappy thought! And the more positive we are, or the more positive things we choose to think with our thoughts, the higher our vibration becomes and then the more powerful we become. How powerful do you feel when you are angry? How powerful do you feel when you are loving? Love is the MOST powerful energy in the universe.

There are millions and millions of different levels of vibration. The tiny particles that make up all energy vibrate. These are called protons, neutrons, and electrons. The whole wide universe vibrates. Everything is vibrating. Human beings, our Mother Earth, your best friend, your cat, your shoes, your hair, your clothes (ooh, that tickles), and every single thing in the universe are all just different degrees of One and the same vibrating energy. Mud vibrates slowly. Light vibrates very fast. Name something that you think is vibrating faster than light.

ENERGY VIBRATES.

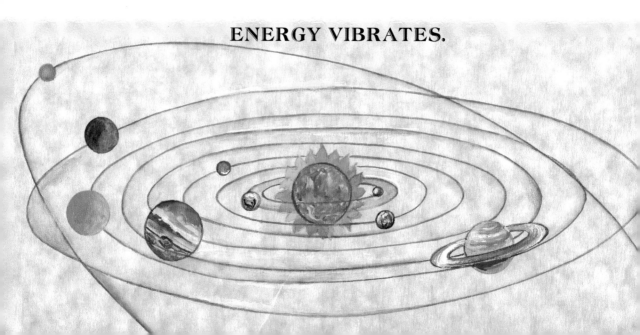

The fourth law is the LAW OF POLARITY. This law means that everything has its opposite. The North Pole and the South Pole are opposite ends of One Earth. Hot and cold are opposites of One thing—temperature. Understanding the law of polarity makes you magically able to turn a negative feeling, like fear, into its positive opposite—faith. You can do this with any feeling that feels bad to you. Just find its positive opposite and you have changed your polarity. Doesn't that feel better?

Name all the opposites you can think of. Do you see how they are all just different degrees of One and the same energy? Like this:

Big and little are different poles of One and the same thing—size. Near and far are different poles of One and the same thing—distance. Black and white are different poles of One and the same thing—color.

EVERYTHING HAS ITS OPPOSITE.

The fifth law is THE LAW OF RHYTHM. Rhythm shows us that there is a flow going on all the time—all around us and within us. There is high tide, then low tide; day, then night; being awake, then being asleep. When we swing on a swing, we go backward, then forward—that's the law of rhythm. When we dance, we move to and fro, side to side, up and down—that's rhythm.

Not too long ago, scientists had an idea about how our universe began. They called this idea the "big bang theory." They thought that way, way, far, far, back in time there was a big explosion and all the stars and the planets and the suns and the galaxies shot out in all directions from this big explosion and that's how it all started. But we could have told them, couldn't we (if they'd only asked), that this idea couldn't be right. We could have told them what Einstein knew—that there can't be a beginning, because, remember, "Energy can neither be created nor destroyed, it simply changes form." So there was no beginning and there can be no ending—just a change of form. So it would be more like a circle. Like God breathing in and breathing out.

And sure enough, another scientist, named Ben Bentov, came up with another idea that explains this perfectly. He showed that it is like a circle. All the things we can see in the universe come down into the level where we can see them (the physical world) and then go back home where they came from (the spiritual world). But each time they go back home they are a little bit smarter, wiser, more complete. So the circle, we then see, is really a spiral.

So, form comes into being (spirit into matter) then form goes back (matter into spirit). This creates TIME.

This is the hourglass—something that measures time. If you play with an hourglass—turning it over and letting the sand drain through, then turning it over again—you are actually playing with this idea of spirit into matter and matter into spirit—or TIME.

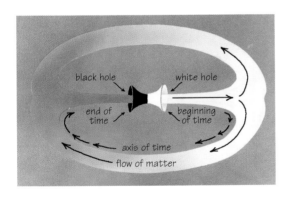

Things are always flowing according to

THE LAW OF RHYTHM.

(Can you find the door in this law?)

spirit into matter

matter into spirit

The sixth law is the LAW OF CAUSE AND EFFECT. This law tells us that there is no such thing as chance—everything happens according to law. This is an orderly universe, governed by the seven laws. For every action we make, there is a reaction. If you hit a baseball, that is an action. When it goes flying across the field, that is the reaction. For every action there is a reaction. For every cause there is an effect.

If we plant a turnip seed, a turnip will grow from it, not an eggplant. When we see the turnip, we know there was first a turnip seed. This a "cause and effect" backward and forward.

If we plant seeds of love, love grows from it, not hate. When we see flowers of love, we know there were first seeds of love.

In the same way, when there is negativity in our life, like anger, disorder, or confusion, we can be sure that somewhere, sometime, we planted

seeds of negativity. We get back exactly what we have planted—no more, no less.

This may seem difficult to accept, especially if there is negativity around us that appears to have nothing to do with us, but our soul chooses situations where we can grow. Sometimes those situations appear very ugly, but, to the soul, learning is the most important thing. So, in the end, what looked very ugly has served a very beautiful purpose. We have learned something valuable.

I bet you can think of lots of examples of this law. Nothing is accidental. All happens according to THE LAW OF CAUSE AND EFFECT. This law is the same thing as the law of "karma" in the Hindu religion. In the Christian tradition, it's what Jesus meant when he said, "As ye sow, so shall ye also reap."

The seventh law is THE LAW OF GENDER. The law of gender is the law of creation. Whenever you have made something, you have used the law of gender. This is how it works: All things have both polarities in them. (Remember the fourth law?) Ideas are feminine. Doing is masculine.

The feminine is like a circle,

 the masculine is like a straight line.

Guess what you get if you unite a circle and a straight line? You get the spiral we spoke of earlier.

The spiral is the symbol for life. It's the same on every level of creation. There must be something feminine and something masculine, put together, to create something new. This is easiest to see when a woman and a man create, from themselves, a new baby.

A battery also must have a negative and a positive pole to generate electricity. It's the same principle.

Did you know that protons have a positive charge and electrons have a negative charge? These are the basic building blocks of all creation—the tiny particles we learned about in the first law. This is gender.

THE LAW OF GENDER IS THE LAW OF CREATION.

Can you explain the law of gender to someone older than you?

If you direct a bright beam of sunlight through a prism, the prism breaks the light up into seven colors. This is like the seven laws.

There is really only One energy—like the sunlight—but here on Earth, it's divided up into seven colors, or laws, like the rainbow.

Each of us can appreciate all the seven laws and use each One of them, but it's important to remember that there's really only

ONE
ENERGY.

See if you can become a Master of the seven laws in your life—then you can help others use The Laws too. (If they ask.)

When all of us know The Laws and use The Laws wisely, we will have made our Earth a very happy place. Hermes would be proud!

So, this is what Herman read in the big book.

He walked quietly over to Diana and thanked her very much for sharing the Laws of Living with him.

"Herman, would you like to have this book?" Diana asked. "This is my own personal copy and you may keep it for your very own if you'd like. I'm giving it to you."

Herman didn't know what to say. He could have his very own Laws of Living?

"Yes, yes, Diana," he finally said. "Yes, may I please?"

"Certainly, Herman." And she carefully placed the big book in Herman's hands.

Herman noticed that there was more in The Book that he hadn't read yet. But, when he turned the page to the next part, all he saw was:

"The First Law: Energy is Always Changing"—and then there was nothing else on the page. It was blank. He turned the page and then saw:

"The Second Law: The Law of Relativity"—and more blank space. The whole rest of The Book seemed to be this way—just the name of the law and nothing after that.

"Why is this Diana? There are no more words after the name of the law. Where are all the rest of the words?" Now Herman was starting to get a little concerned. He didn't want an incomplete book. He wanted to know everything about The Laws. So where were the words!

Diana looked at him patiently and asked him this question, "Herman, are you sure you want to learn The Laws?"

For Heavens sake! Of course he was sure. This is all he'd wanted his whole life—all seven years of it! So he told her so.

"Well, Herman, it's all there."

"What?" Herman said, with a look of total bewilderment on his face. He looked at Diana. He looked at The Book. He looked at Diana. He looked back at The Book. He took off his glasses and cleaned them very hard. He looked back at The Book again—blank pages?!

Now he looked at Diana and he could feel tears starting to come to his eyes. "Why is this thing happening?" he thought. "Are the words invisible? What does this mean?"

"But, Diana, I can't see the . . ." he stammered and shuffled and was very uncomfortable.

"Herman, you must write the words."

"What . . . me?"

"Yes, you."

"But the, but . . ." Herman did not understand.

"Herman, if you truly want to know The Laws, you must fill in the blank spaces." Then Diana repeated what she said before. "This magic is not something that can be described. It can only be experienced by the One practicing the law. If you do this, if you use The Laws, you will experience the magic too. Now do you understand, Herman?" asked Diana.

Herman thought that maybe he was beginning to understand. He knew there were questions The Book had asked him. And he knew that he could answer some of them and some of them he could not. Like the one about "the door" in the fifth law. He had no idea what the answer to that one was. So maybe he was supposed to study The Laws.

The Seven Laws
of
The Universe

"Am I supposed to study The Laws, Diana?" Herman shyly asked.

"Exactly, Herman. You cannot simply read The Book and expect to be a Master. You will only become a Master once you've proven The Laws to yourself," Diana replied.

"So, the blank spaces are for me to write what I learn when I experiment with each of The Laws?" Herman asked.

"Right again, Herman." And Diana smiled. "You see, Herman, even though The Laws are as real as gravity, you can only work with gravity if you understand it fully. We overcome gravity every time we fly in an airplane, yet gravity first had to be thoroughly understood before we could do that. The Laws are just words on paper until you try them, test them, and show them—in your own experience—to be true. Then, and only then, can you expect to master them.

"The blank spaces on the pages are for you. They are your own personal workbook."

Then Diana taught Herman a new word. The word was "alchemist." "For a very long time, all down through history," she said, "people thought that an alchemist was a person who was trying to turn simple metals (like lead) into gold. The alchemists were considered to be very strange folks indeed. Most people feared them, and in some cases the alchemists were even harmed. But," Diana said, "the truth is that the alchemists were really ones who were trying, themselves, to be Masters. And they knew that, once they had mastered The Laws of their own being, they were, indeed, changing something into gold. Their own souls."

Herman thought carefully about all Diana had told him. He walked over to the big window in the library and looked out at the bright sunshine. He remembered the part of The Book that taught that the seven laws were like sunshine through a prism. Then Herman did a very bold thing.

He looked at the sunlight and made a decision.

"I will be a Master."

And someday, I will tell you the story of how he did it. . . .

Will you be a Master too?

The First Law: Energy is Always Changing

The Second Law: The Law of Relativity

THE THIRD LAW: THE LAW OF VIBRATION

THE FOURTH LAW: THE LAW OF POLARITY

THE FIFTH LAW: THE LAW OF RHYTHM

THE SIXTH LAW: THE LAW OF CAUSE AND EFFECT

THE SEVENTH LAW: THE LAW OF GENDER

SUGGESTED RESOURCE

This book would not be complete without my most sincere and deepest gratitude to one man—Dr. George Thurman Fleet—the originator of a class entitled "Concept-Therapy."

Though I never actually got to meet Dr. Fleet, I was privileged to take my first CT class in 1971, and I learned there the seven laws. This information fundamentally changed my life for the better.

Dr. Fleet acknowledged having learned The Laws from the ancient Hermetic philosophy. The founder of this teaching was known as "Hermes" in ancient Greece, and "Thoth" in ancient Egypt. All of today's major religions evolved from and take their basic precepts from the Hermetic principles, but Dr. Fleet is responsible for bringing this ancient wisdom to the modern world once again and in a form made practical for all who wish to become Masters of their own being.

I hope I have continued the tradition that my mentors—Hermes and Dr. Fleet—began in a way that is pleasing to both of them and to you, the Seeker.

Most of all, I hope I have been successful in giving to the children of the world a clear picture of the Oneness of All Life.

For further information on Concept-Therapy and Conceptology contact:

The Concept Therapy Institute
25550 Boerne Stage Road
San Antonio, TX 78255
1-800-531-5628